CLAUDE DEBUSSY

(1862-1918)

SELECTED WORKS FOR PIANO

Compiled and Edited by Keith Snell

CONTENTS

*The title *Le petit Noir* has been translated from the original title into contemporary French vernacular.

For supplementary study, a recording is available on compact disc, performed by pianist Diane Hidy (GP380CD). Ms. Hidy's performance is closely matched to this edition as a practical example for students.

ISBN 0-8497-6195-6

© 1995 Neil A. Kjos Music Company, 4380 Jutland Drive, San Diego, California 92117-0894
International copyright secured. All rights reserved. Printed in U.S.A.

MUSICAL IMPRESSIONISM

Debussy is regarded as the creator and leading figure of musical Impressionism, despite the fact that he deplored the term and denied his role in the movement. Like Monet in painting and Mallarmé in poetry, Debussy introduced a new style of composition. His many novel musical devices include the use of the Oriental pentatonic scale, the whole-tone scale, consecutive parallel chords and intervals, unresolved harmonies and the abandonment of traditional form.

CLAUDE DEBUSSY (1862-1918)

Claude Debussy was born in 1862 in St.-Germain-on-Laye, France. His first piano teacher was Mme. Mauté de Fleurville—a student of Chopin and mother-in-law of the Symbolist poet Verlaine. She recognized his musical talents and encouraged him to enter the Conservetoire Nationale in 1872 when he was 10 years old.

When Debussy was 18, he became a piano teacher for the children of Mme. Nadezhda von Meck, Tchaikovsky's patroness. In the summers of 1881 and 1882, Debussy traveled with her family to their summer estate in Moscow. While he was there, he became familiar with the music of Borodin and Mussorgsky, which subsequently influenced his compositional style.

In 1888 and 1889, Debussy was again influenced by non-western music styles. His travels to Bayreuth and his introduction to the Javanese gamelan at the Paris Exposition became inspirations for underlying elements in his music and influenced his taste for exotic musical colors. About this time, Debussy became friends with French poets of the symbolist school, and was particularly fascinated by Mallarmé. Debussy's contact with Impressionist artists added to the influence of modern French poetry and contributed to his mature style.

In 1899, Debussy married Rosalie Texier. However, in 1904 he left her for Mme. Emma Bardac. Rosalie shot herself in despair, but did recover and later divorced him. Debussy and Mme. Bardac eventually were married. Together they had a daughter, Chouchou, to whom Debussy dedicated his Children's Corner. Chouchou died at the age of fourteen.

In 1914, Debussy contemplated an American tour with violinist Arthur Hartmann, but gave up the idea due to illness. Thereafter his health continued to fail as a result of cancer. His last public appearance was on May 5, 1917, when he played the piano part of his Violin Sonata. He died in Paris in the spring of 1918, toward the end of World War I.

GLOSSARY OF FRENCH TERMS

animé: Animated, lively.

animez un peu: Become a little animated, lively.

arabesque: A florid musical passage.

assez modéré: Very moderately.

au movement: Return to the original tempo, *a tempo*.

augmentez progressivement: Crescendo continually.

avec une grande émotion: With much emotion.

calmant: Subsiding, becoming calm.

cédez: Slowing down, *rallentando*.

Clair de lune: Moonlight

comme un écho de la phrase entendue précédement: Like an echo of the preceding phrase.

dans la sonorité du début: With the sound (tone quality, resonance, sonority) of the beginning.

dans une brume doucement sonore: In a softly resonant mist.

dans une expression allant grandissant: With an expression that becomes larger and larger.

doux: Sweet, gentle, *dolce*.

doux et expressif: Gentle and expressive.

doux et fluide: Gentle and flowing.

doux et triste: Gentle (sweet) and sad.

égal et sans sécheresse: Even and without dryness.

en animant: Becoming lively, animated.

en conservant le rythme: Maintaining (preserving) the rhythm.

en dehors: In the foreground, emphasized.

en diminuant: Decreasing volume, *diminuendo*.

estompe: Blurred, indistinct. Subdued.

et: and

expressif et concentré: expressive and concentrated (focused, intense).

flottant et sourd: Floating and muted

gauche: Awkward.

léger et gracieux: Light and graceful.

m.d.(main droite): Right hand.

m.g.(main gauche): Left hand.

mais: But.

marqué: Emphasized, *marcato*.

modérément animé: Moderately lively, somewhat animated.

morendo jusqu'à la fin: Dying away until the end.

murmuré et en retenant peu à peu: Whispered (murmured) and slow down little by little.

nuance: Subtle variety of shading, tempo, touch, dynamic, etc..

peu à peu: Little by little.

peu à peu sortant de la brume: Little by little emerging from the mist.

plus: More.

plus movementé: Faster.

profondément calme: Profoundly calm.

retenez: Become slower.

retenu: Slower.

sans: Without

sans dureté: Without harshness.

sans lenteur: Without slowness, delay.

sans lourdeur: Without heaviness.

sans nuances: Without nuances.

sans presser: Without rushing.

sans rigueur: Without rigidity or strictness; freely.

sonore: Resonant.

toujours: Always; Still; Nevertheless.

toujours retenu: Always holding back.

très animé: very animated, lively.

très calme et doucement expressif: very calm and gently expressive.

très doux: Very sweet, gentle.

très doux et délicatement expressif: very sweet (gentle) and delicately expressive.

très expressif: very expressive

très léger: very light.

très modéré: very moderately.

très net et très sec: very clear and very dry.

très rythmé: very rythmical.

Un peu animé: A little animated.

un peu moins lent: A little less slow; slightly faster.

un peu moins vite; A little less rapid; slightly slower.

un peu retenu: A little slower.

LE PETIT NOIR

ARABESQUE No. 1

8

10

GP380

ARABESQUE No. 2

Allegretto scherzando

RÊVERIE

THE GIRL WITH THE FLAXEN HAIR

(La Fille aux cheveux de lin)

from "Preludes, Book 1"

THE SUNKEN CATHEDRAL

(La Cathédrale Engloutie)

from "Preludes, Book 1"

Profondément (Dans une brume doucement sonore)

Peu à peu sortant de la brume

Augmentez progressivement (Sans presser)

Sonore sans dureté

Un peu moins lent (Dans une expression allant grandissant)

Dans la sonorité du début

CHILDREN'S CORNER (*Suite for Piano*)

I. Doctor Gradus ad Parnassum

L. H. over R. H.

Un peu retenu

a Tempo

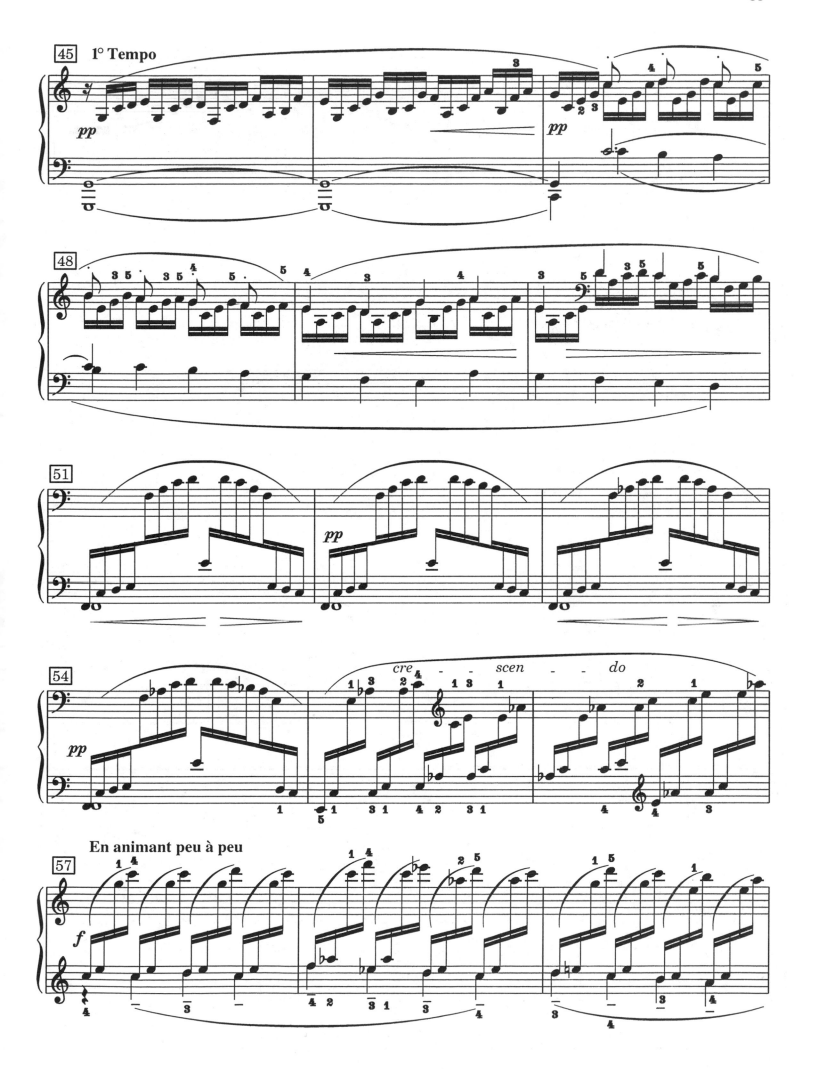

Très animé

II. Jimbo's Lullaby

Assez modéré

p *doux et un peu gauche*

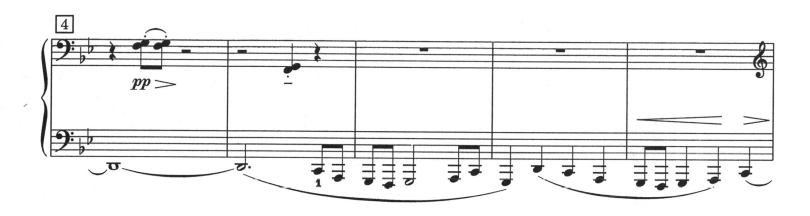

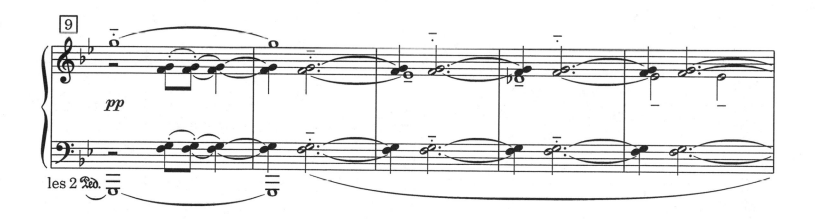

les 2 Péd.

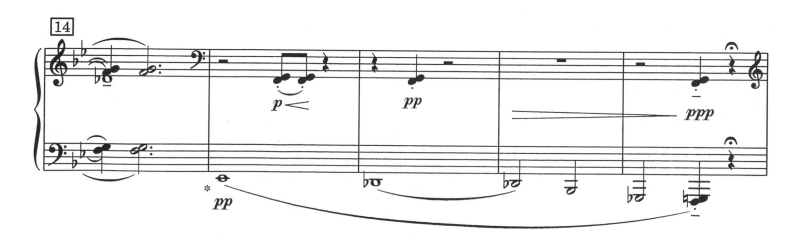

III. Serenade for the Doll

(*) *Il faudra mettre la pèdale sourde pendant toute la durèe de ce morceau, mème aux endroits marquès d'un* **f**.
(The soft pedal must be held down for the entire duration of the piece, even in the sections marked *forte*.)

IV. The Snow is Dancing

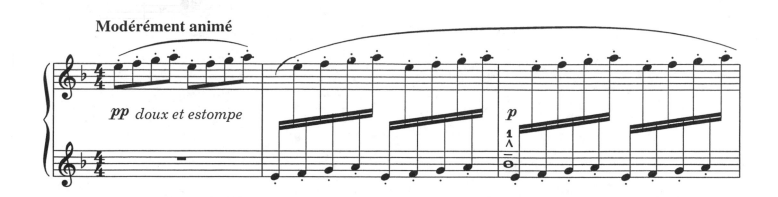

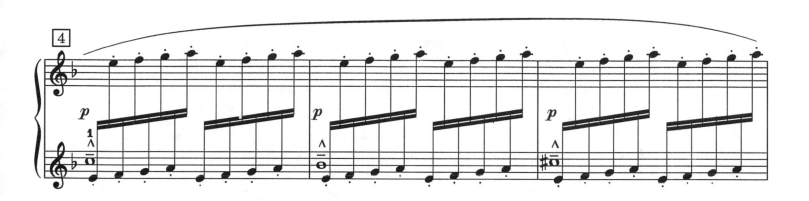

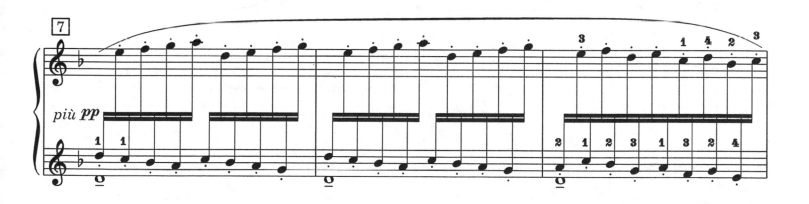

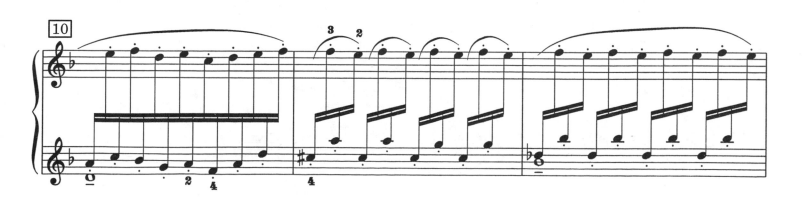

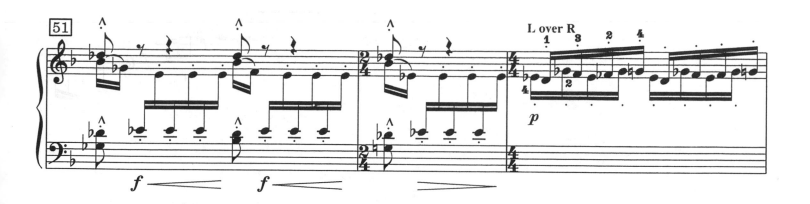

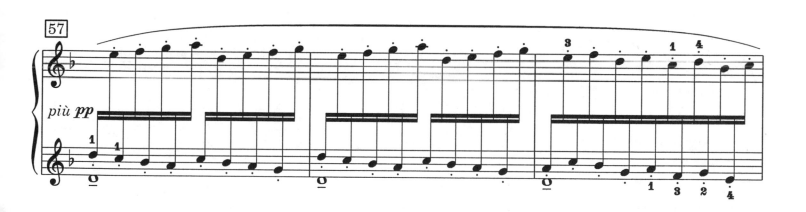

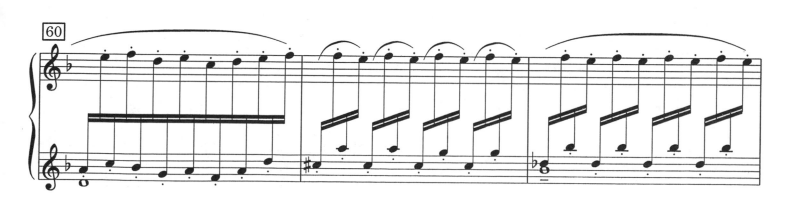

V. The Little Shepherd

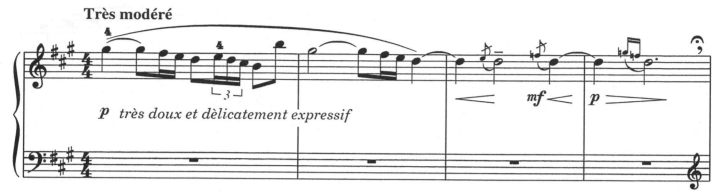

VI. Golliwogg's Cake-walk

CLAIR DE LUNE

ABOUT THIS EDITION

- This edition is based on the first editions published by Durand. All selections are in their original form. No arrangements or simplifications are used.

- The editor chose to keep all tempo and expression marks exactly as they appear in the original editions. A French-English glossary is provided to assist in understandiing the French terms.

- Fingerings are added by the editor.

- No pedal indications are found in the original editions. A few pedal marks are added by the editor. Due to the often elusive pedal technique required in this music, it is difficult to successfully translate many pedaling instructions to the printed page. A keen ear and a sense of imagination will be the best guide for successful pedaling.